The well known parable of the Good Samaritan
is retold simply in this delightfully illustrated
version and will appeal to all young listeners
and early readers.

The story is based on the gospel of St Luke,
chapter 10, verses 30-37.

British Library Cataloguing in Publication Data
Hately, David
     The good Samaritan.
     1. Bible. N.T. Parables: Good Samaritan
     I. Title   II. Burton, Terry   III. Series
     226'.8
     ISBN 0-7214-9587-7

First Edition

Published by Ladybird Books Ltd Loughborough Leicestershire UK
Ladybird Books Inc Auburn Maine 04210 USA
© LADYBIRD BOOKS LTD MCMLXXXIX
Printed in England

The Good Samaritan

written by DAVID HATELY
illustrated by TERRY BURTON

Ladybird Books

A road between two towns led through a lonely wasteland.

Some wicked men had made their home there. They were always on the lookout for any travellers passing by.

They lay in wait to attack and rob the travellers.

There was once a man who had to travel down the road from one town to the other.

As he passed through the lonely wasteland, the robbers attacked him. They beat him and took all his possessions.

Then they ran away and left him lying wounded on the road.

Down the road came someone from the same town as the first traveller.

Everyone thought he was a very good man. He was always in church where everyone could see him saying his prayers.

He didn't stop when he saw the traveller lying there in the road. He hurried on his way as fast as he could.

Later, another man from the same town came along the road.

He was said to be very holy by all who knew him. He liked to help in church by serving at the altar where everyone could see him.

When the man saw the traveller lying wounded in the road, he did not stop. He hurried past as quickly as he could.

By now the traveller was half dead from his wounds. He lay on the road covered in blood.

Along the road came another man, riding a donkey.

He was a stranger, and had only been passing through the town where the others lived.

When he saw the man lying wounded on the road, he stopped to see if he could help.

The stranger's heart was filled with pity for the wounded man. He saw at once that he needed help.

He cleaned the man's wounds as best he could. Then he made some bandages by tearing his robe into strips of cloth.

But the stranger knew that the man might die and that he needed looking after.

When he had cleaned the wounds and bandaged them, he lifted the man onto the donkey's back.

Going slowly, so that the wounded man would be as comfortable as possible, they made their way along the road.

When they had travelled safely through the wasteland where the robbers lived, they came to an inn.

The stranger lifted the wounded man from the donkey and carried him inside.

He gave the innkeeper some money, and said,
"Here is enough money to pay for this man to
stay for two days. Look after him until
come back."

The stranger hurried on his way.

It took him longer than he expected to finish his business. But as soon as he could, he went back to the inn and gave the innkeeper more money, enough to care for the man until he was better.

Who was a real neighbour to the man attacked by robbers?

Was it the first man, who passed by and did not stop to help his fellow townsman?

Was it the second man? Or was it the stranger?

This story about the travellers was first told by Jesus. In his story, the stranger came from a place called Samaria, so we often call him the 'Good Samaritan'.

When Jesus asked the people who were listening to the story who they thought was a real neighbour to the wounded man, they answered, ''It was the stranger, because he helped the wounded man.''

Jesus agreed with them, and said we must all try to be like the Good Samaritan. We must do everything we can to help those who are in trouble.

For he said that we must love God with all our heart. But we have to prove it by loving our neighbour as much as we love ourselves.